FROM THE AWARD-WINNING
AUTHORS OF I HERO COMES...

YOU CRACK THE CASE

TIGER'S LAIR

STEVE BARLOW & STEVE SKIDMORE
ILLUSTRATED BY DAVID COUSENS

First published in 2011
by Franklin Watts

Text © Steve Barlow and Steve Skidmore 2011
Illustrations by David Cousens © Franklin Watts 2011
Cover design by Peter Scoulding

Franklin Watts
338 Euston Road
London NW1 3BH

Franklin Watts Australia
Level 17/207 Kent Street
Sydney, NSW 2000

A CIP catalogue record for this book
is available from the British Library.

ISBN: 978 0 7496 9284 1

1 3 5 7 9 10 8 6 4 2

Printed in Great Britain

Franklin Watts is a division of Hachette Children's Books,
an Hachette UK company.
www.hachette.co.uk

An adventure where YOU crack the case!

This book is not like others you may have read. In this story YOU have to make decisions to solve the crime. Each section of this book is numbered. At the end of each section, YOU will have to make a choice. The choice YOU make will lead to a different section of the book.

Some choices will be correct, others will not. You must make the right choices by looking at the evidence, solving puzzles or even breaking codes. Make sure that you LOOK carefully at the pictures – they *could* give you vital clues.

If you make a bad decision you may receive a warning from your boss, or get thrown off the case. Some of your decisions could even be FATAL!

Record how many BAD DECISIONS and WARNINGS you get from your boss. When you have cracked the case – or been kicked off it – you'll get a Crime Team Agent Rating that will show how well – or how badly – you've done.

You are the leader of Crime Team, a section of the International Police Federation based in New York City, USA. You are one of the world's leading experts in cracking cases that no one else can. You have solved crimes across the globe and have made many enemies, who would like to see you dead...

YOUR MISSION
» To aid and support national police forces anywhere in the world.
» To tackle the toughest cases and solve mysteries that others cannot.

YOUR TEAM
Your team contains the best of the best – top investigative experts from around the world. You can use up to three of these on any case... You will have to make decisions about whose skills will be best suited to help solve the crime.

YOUR BOSS
COMMANDER TUCKER

Ex-military, ex-New York Police Department, ex-CIA and currently your bad-ass boss. Given half a chance, Commander Tucker will chew your butt. He will alert you to BAD DECISIONS and give you WARNINGS. He might even THROW YOU OFF the case!

YOUR SIDEKICK
LEON PEREZ

JOB: Your constant sidekick and legman – Leon does all the stuff you're too busy to do yourself and is also the "muscle".

EXPERTISE: A ballistics expert with a wide knowledge of all types of weapon.

NOTES: It is said he can smell a bullet and tell you which gun it came from – he's that good!

DOCTOR ANUSHA DAS

JOB: Forensic pathologist

EXPERTISE: Brilliant at establishing the time and cause of death of a victim.

NOTES: Extensive knowledge of poisons and diseases.

SUN LIN

JOB: Forensic scientist

EXPERTISE: An expert at fingerprinting, DNA analysis and other forensic techniques.

NOTES: Has the ability to remember everything she has seen or heard. Never forgets a face, remembers every crime report and excellent at finding all kinds of information.

DARIUS KING ("BUGS")

JOB: Computer expert

EXPERTISE: A genius at hacking, data retrieval and electronic surveillance.

NOTES: Is an expert in using computers to help with HID (Human Identification at a Distance) to identify suspects and criminals.

TODD BLACKWOOD

JOB: Profiler (forensic psychologist)

EXPERTISE: Can "get inside" the minds of criminals and predict what they will do next.

NOTES: Also an expert in espionage, counter-espionage and terrorism.

» **NOW GO TO SECTION 1.**

1

You are flying back from a successful Crime Team investigation in Sydney, Australia, and are looking forward to a well-earned rest. Your sidekick, Leon Perez, and computer expert, Darius "Bugs" King, are travelling with you. As usual, Perez is moaning. This time it's about Commander Tucker, your boss.

"Why did we have to take a scheduled flight? Why couldn't Tucker hire a private jet for us?"

"Tucker giving us a private jet?" you reply. "Since when did he go soft in the head? And I wish you'd stop moaning, Leon. I need to get some sleep and you're bugging me."

"No, that's Bugs's job," replies Perez. "He's the computer genius in the team. Aren't you, Bugs?"

Bugs groans at Leon's attempt at humour.

You shake your head. "You're not funny either."

"Man, you are seriously stressed – I reckon you need that holiday."

"A holiday from your constant moaning would be great," you reply.

Before Perez can reply, the plane turns sharply, causing him to spill his drink. "What the…?"

You glance out of the window. "Why are we turning off course?" you mutter.

A flight attendant approaches and hands you a satellite phone. "For you, sir."

You take the phone. "Hope I didn't wake you," a voice growls. It's Tucker!

"No such luck. I'm too tired to sleep. I need a holiday," you reply.

"You can take a break when I'm done with you," Tucker snaps. "A case has just come in… I need you and the team to crack it."

» **If you want to ask for a holiday, go to 25.**
» **If you want to take the case, go to 33.**

2

"You'd better go and talk to him, Sun Lin," you say. "He'll recognise me – he saw me at the airport when I arrived. Todd, you stay close for backup." You hand Sun Lin a micro two-way radio. "Get him talking," you tell her.

Sun Lin nods. "What should I say, boss? Should I tell him that I've got a message from Fang Da? Or should I say that Chen has sent me to sort out the ransom?"

You think. The man is obviously not expecting you, and you don't know for sure that Fang Da is involved. So should you mention Samuel Chen? Who should you say Sun Lin has a message from?

» **If you want her to mention Fang Da, go to 20.**
» **If you want her to mention Chen, go to 32.**

3

Sun Lin and Blackwood soon arrive and you all head over to the Ritz Carlton Hotel. You take the MTR railway system.

Before you are allowed to see Chen, his bodyguards take away your weapons and equipment. You protest, but they will not take no for an answer.

Soon you are in Samuel Chen's top floor suite, looking out over Hong Kong harbour. Chen and his bodyguards watch you suspiciously. After introducing the team, you ask Chen to tell you about his daughter.

"My daughter Ruby is fifteen years old. She was supposed to be meeting me for lunch yesterday, but she never turned up. I swear I will kill those who have kidnapped her. I am known as the Tiger, and I will act as ruthlessly as my namesake! These dogs have demanded a ransom for her of 3 million dollars. A note was delivered – I have had it translated for you."

"So do you have any idea who might be responsible?" you ask.

Chen scowls. "I have many enemies, but there is one man who hates me above the rest. His name is Fang Da. He is known as the Dragon. Once we were business partners and friends, but

he claimed that I cheated him. No one makes such accusations against me. I ruined him and his reputation, and now he is my mortal enemy."

You look at Blackwood. "What do you think, Todd?"

"If Fang Da is responsible for the kidnap, then the ransom is a blind," replies Blackwood. "He will take the money and still kill the girl."

Chen looks angry. "He would not dare!"

Blackwood shakes his head. "It's a classic revenge case. Don't pay – at least not yet."

» **If you think Todd is right, go to 27.**

» **To tell Chen to pay the ransom, go to 31.**

4

"Let's go," you tell the others. You charge at the door and kick it open.

You burst into the room to see a group of men. Several are armed! You have made a big mistake! The tailor had a dragon tattoo – he is a member of Fang Da's triad gang!

Before you can react one of them fires a shot. It hits your shoulder. Perez fires back and drops the man, but the others reach for their guns and shoot you and your team down.

» **The Crime Team is dead! To start again, go to 1.**

5

Hours later, you wake up to find that your arms and legs are bound tightly. Your body aches and you feel weak. You are lying on a wooden floor and you hear the sound of water from outside. Even though you are dazed, you realise that you must be in the hold of a moving boat.

A door opens and a man enters. He is wearing a dark suit and holding a case. He kicks you in the stomach, causing you to retch.

Another man joins him and they pick you up – you try to struggle, but it is hopeless. The two men manhandle you up some stairs onto the deck of a small Chinese junk.

It is dark outside. The lights of the city are in the distance – you are off one of the many of Hong Kong's small islands.

You continue to struggle, and shout, but there is no one to help you. You know that this is the end for you. In an instant, you are tipped over the side of the boat into the cold, deadly sea.

» **You have failed in your mission and paid the ultimate price. Start this case again by going back to 1.**

6

You take the train and are soon at the cable car station. There are many people hanging around, including children.

You glance at your watch — it is nearly 3 p.m. — the time you think that the dead man was supposed to meet his contact. You scan the crowd, looking for a clue — perhaps there will be someone you'll recognise?

» **If you think that there is someone you should approach, go to 39.**

» **If you want to check what Perez and Bugs have come up with, go to 13.**

7

You take out your gun, causing the other passengers to panic.

They jostle you as you try to take aim at the man in the cabin below. You fire off several shots, but it is useless – you cannot get a clear shot.

You cry out as you see Sun Lin being picked up and pushed out of the car. You watch helplessly as she plunges to her death. The man in the car looks at you and smiles before jumping to his own death.

You stand shocked as the passengers huddle in a corner of the cabin.

Many hours later, you and the rest of the team are sitting in an office of the Hong Kong police department, trying to explain the events that led up to Sun Lin's death. An officer comes in and hands you a phone. It is Tucker.

"Ruby Chen's body has been found – her father is holding you responsible. Not only that, you sent one of my best team members to her death… When the police have finished with you, get your sorry ass back here and clear your desk. I don't need someone like you on my team."

» **You have failed and caused the death of one of your team. To see how you rate as a detective, go to 46.**

8

"I'll take Blackwood," you tell Tucker.

"That's the right choice," he replies. "He'll be able to put together a profile on the kidnappers and Chen."

"And his knowledge of counterespionage will be useful if the Chinese Government are involved. How long before Sun Lin and Blackwood will be in Hong Kong?" you ask.

"They should be with you soon. They're in Japan on a case, so I'll hire a private jet for them…"

Great, you think, I'd better not tell Perez. Tucker continues. "I'll send more information when you get to Hong Kong. There will be a driver waiting for you at the airport. The password is 'Tiger'."

"Why Tiger?" you ask.

"That's what we're calling the case. It's what Chen likes to call himself – the tiger can be a symbol of power and wealth. He likes to remind people he's a top man. Remember that when dealing with him. Don't upset him."

"Would I?" you ask and ring off.

You tell Perez and Bugs the "good" news and then close your eyes, trying to get some much needed rest before the case begins.

» **Go to 38.**

9

An hour later, your phone rings – it is Tucker. He is furious.

"The police have just found Ruby Chen's body. By rushing in like a bull in a china shop – and don't even think I'm trying to be funny – you caused the kidnapper to panic. Everyone, and I mean everyone, is calling for your head. Get back here and clear your desk – you're out."

» **You have failed! To see how you rate as a detective, go to 46.**

10

"Can you get anything from the burnt paper?" you ask Sun Lin.

She looks at the mass of paper. "Not easily, but I think I've got some equipment that could help us out. Todd – pass me the case with the portable lab."

Using chemicals and a digital scanner, Sun Lin soon creates a faint image from the burnt paper and uses an infrared magnifier to reveal the outline of a map.

"Ruby!" says Bugs. "But what's the map?"

"It's part of the Hong Kong train system," says Sun Lin.

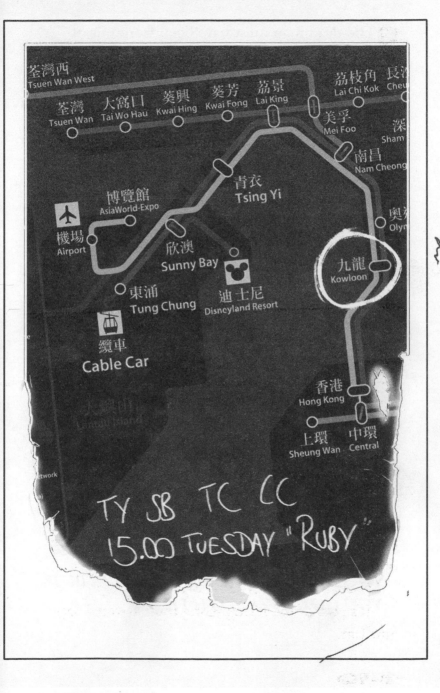

"The dead man must have been from out of town if he needed a map," you say.

"What are those initials?" asks Perez.

"They must mean something," you say, staring at the map. "Maybe they tell us where he was going to be at fifteen hundred hours on Tuesday." You look carefully at the map and a thought strikes you. "I think I know where he was going!"

» **If you think the man was heading for Disneyland, go to 44.**

» **If you think he was heading for the cable car, go to 23.**

11

"Put the phone away, Bugs," you say.

He shakes his head and keeps a finger to his lips.

Chen is amazed. "You obviously do not have control of your team," he says. "Perhaps I need to tell Tucker that you are not up to this job."

You realise that you cannot show weakness in front of Chen. You try to rescue the situation. "No, I trust my team. I suggest we do what he says and keep quiet."

Chen grunts but says no more.

» **YOU NEARLY MADE A MISTAKE, *BUT YOU GOT AWAY WITH IT!***
Go to 41.

12

You watch as the man and Sun Lin get into the cable car. They wait briefly before the car begins to climb up the mountain.

Todd hurries over to you. "Boss, shouldn't we follow them?"

You shake your head and pull out a pair of binoculars from your case so you can watch the cable car's progress. "I don't want to scare him off, he knows me."

"But Sun Lin is up there on her own."

"She'll be fine," you say, but your words stick in your throat as a scream erupts from your radio. You look up and see Sun Lin fighting with the man! He wasn't fooled!

"Sun Lin!" you shout into your radio, but there is silence as her screams are cut off. In the distance, you see the man fighting with Sun Lin, before he drags her over to the window. You stare in disbelief as you see her body being thrown from the cable car and tumbling towards the ground.

Todd stares at you in horror.

Many hours later, you and the team are sitting in an office of the Hong Kong police department, trying to explain the events that led up to Sun Lin's death. An officer comes in and hands you a phone. It is Tucker.

There is a quiet anger in his voice. "Ruby Chen's body has been found – her father is holding you responsible. Not only that, you sent one of my best team members to her death... When the police have finished with you, get your sorry ass back here and clear your desk. I don't need someone like you on my team."

» **You have failed and caused the death of one of your team. To see how you rate as a detective, go to 46.**

13

"OK. I'm going to contact Bugs and Leon," you tell the others. "You two keep your eyes open for anyone acting suspiciously." You move away to a quiet area where there is no one else around, and pull out your mobile phone.

As you do, you hear a noise behind you. You turn. There is a man standing in front of you with a gun. It is the man with spiky hair who had the dragon sign at the airport! You are too slow to react as he brings his gun down onto your head. In an explosion of light and pain, you drop to the floor, unconscious.

» **Go to 5.**

14

"I'll take Das," you say.

"Are you crazy?" shouts Tucker. "Das is a pathologist! What use is a pathologist if there's no body for her to examine?" Tucker pauses. "Though if you make another dumb decision, there probably will be one – yours!"

You realise you've made a bad choice. "I told you I need a break, boss," you say. "I'm not thinking straight."

"Then start thinking straight! I don't want any foul ups on this case! So who are you gonna take?"

» YOU'VE MADE A BAD DECISION!

Make a note of this and go to 8.

15

You shake your head at the man. "You've got a dragon tattoo. You're a member of Fang Da's gang and members of it we've already met were ready to die rather than betray their leader. You've given me the information far too easily. I think we'll head up the stairs."

He jumps at you, but a quick knife-hand chop sends him crashing to the floor. You turn to Bugs. "Keep an eye on him. If he moves or makes a sound, you know what to do…"

Carefully and quietly, you and the others head

up the stairs. They lead to a landing with two apartment doors.

"Which one, boss?" asks Perez. "Should we go into both at the same time?"

You shake your head. "Not enough of us – we don't know how many people are behind those doors – we can't be sure we'd rescue Ruby and we don't have enough time to get backup."

"So which one do we go into?" hisses Perez. "If we get it wrong, I reckon we'll have a dead kid on our hands…"

"Those are Chinese symbols above the doors," says Sun Lin. "Left is earth, the right is fire."

Todd whispers. "There will be a reason, why Fang Da has chosen one apartment over the other. We need to make a connection between him and the two symbols."

You think about the symbols and their possible connection with Fang Da. Which apartment should you go into?

» **If you wish to go into the apartment with the earth symbol, go to 42.**

» **If you wish to go into the apartment with the fire symbol, go to 29.**

16

"We'll split into two groups," you tell the others.
"Sun Lin, you and I will take this floor. Todd,
Leon and Bugs, you take the lower floor."

"How will you get into the rooms?" asks Chen.

"We have our ways," you smile. "Todd, have
you got something for us?"

Blackwood reaches into his equipment case and
takes out a set of electronic key cards. "These will
get us in." He passes them out to the team and
you split up to search for whoever was listening in.

You and Sun Lin head to the room next to
Chen's suite. Gun ready, you slide the electronic
key card into the door lock. The door clicks open.
Should you go in together or should you go in on
your own?

» **If you want to enter the room on your
own, go to 37.**

» **If you decide both of you should go into
the room, go to 30.**

You realise that the man must have been burning
something important. You quickly beat out the
flames in the bin, but the paper is nearly destroyed.

"He must have guessed that we were onto
him when I found the bug. He's tried to destroy
evidence," says Sun Lin.

You nod. You radio down to the team to come
up to the room, then you examine the dead man.
There is nothing in his pockets. As you pull up his
sleeve, you see a tattoo on his forearm.

"That's the symbol for a dragon," says Sun Lin.

"According to Chen, Fang Da calls himself the Dragon," you say.

The team begin to arrive. You explain what happened.

Perez shakes his head. "So all we've got is a dead man and a piece of burnt paper. Looks like we've hit a dead end."

» **If you wish to tell Tucker that you have no leads, go to 40.**

» **To try to retrieve some information from the burnt paper, go to 10.**

18

To the other passengers' amazement, you take off your belt and climb out of the cabin onto the roof. You loop the belt over the cable and slide down towards the cable car where Sun Lin is desperately fighting for her life.

Luckily, the man does not notice you until you smash through the window of the cabin. He pushes Sun Lin away and begins to fight you.

You manage to land some blows, but his martial arts skills are a match for yours.

As he launches a series of lightning kicks on you, Sun Lin recovers enough to smash him on the head with her gun.

He staggers back against the smashed window and begins to topple out of the cabin. You reach forward and grab at his jacket, but it is too late. The cloth rips and the man plunges to his death.

"Are you OK?" you ask Sun Lin.

She nods. "He must have known who I was all along."

"At least that tells us that we're dealing with Fang Da," you say. At that moment your phone rings.

It is Perez. You tell him what has happened and ask him if he and Bugs have made progress.

"We've got a lead. We think Fang Da has an apartment above a tailor's shop in Mong Kok. The problem is – there are a lot of tailor's shops there…"

» **If you think you know where Fang Da might be, go to 21.**

» **If you want to tell Perez to keep looking, go to 36.**

19

You point at the woman holding the card with the tiger symbol. "That's our contact," you say. You, Perez and Bugs head over to her.

"Tiger?" you say.

She nods. "I'm Lucy," she replies. "I'm your driver. I'm to take you to your hotel."

She takes you to a limousine.

"Now, this is more like it," says Perez as he settles in and stretches out.

Soon the limousine is heading into the heart

of Hong Kong and the check-in at The Peninsula Hotel.

"At least they've booked us into somewhere nice," says Perez as the limousine pulls up outside.

You check in and are soon in your room. Once you've unpacked, you have a meeting with Perez and Bugs to discuss what you should do.

"We need to interview Chen," says Bugs. "He's our link to the case, we need to interview him as soon as possible."

Perez disagrees. "Chen is a gangster and traitor. We should keep him at arm's length. He's not trustworthy. Let's head to the police first and see what they say."

Just then your phone rings. It is Tucker. He tells you that Sun Lin and Todd will be in Hong Kong within the next two hours. "What are you planning to do?" he asks.

» **If you want to interview Chen, go to 35.**
» **If you want to make contact with the police first, go to 28.**

20

"Tell him that you have news for Fang Da," you tell Sun Lin. "It's a risk, but you can tell him that the man at the hotel was spotted and has had to go underground."

"And you won't be lying," jokes Todd. "He is going underground – in a coffin."

You smile. "Tell him that you are the new contact and you need to speak to Fang Da immediately. OK – make contact."

You follow Sun Lin at a distance. She approaches the man and begins to talk to him. At first he looks around, suspiciously, but Sun Lin continues to explain the situation just as you told her to. After a couple of minutes, the man nods in agreement and points at the cable car.

You hear Sun Lin say, "OK, let's go to the monastery." She and the man head towards the cable car station.

» **If you wish to take the cable car, go to 24.**
» **If you wish to stay on the ground, go to 12.**

21

"I think I know where Fang Da is," you tell Perez.

Leon sounds surprised. "How?"

"The dead man's jacket – there is the name and address of a tailor. It's a shot in the dark, but it's the best we have…" You tell Leon to get there and you will join them. You also get in touch with Todd and tell him to meet you in Mong Kok.

The cable car reaches its destination and you and Sun Lin get out. You see some people from

the cabin that you were in, pointing you out to a
policeman, so you and Sun Lin quickly dive into
a taxi and head back to the mainland. On the way
to Mong Kok, Leon rings and tells you the address
of the tailor. Soon you are outside the Dragon
Tailors on Canton Road with the rest of the team.

"We've not seen anything suspicious," says Leon.

You head into the shop. The man behind the counter looks up. "Can I help you?" he asks.

You decide that there is no time for messing around. You put a gun to his head. "I want to know where Fang Da is. Tell me or else!"

The man looks surprised. "I don't know what you are talking about."

"Don't lie. I'm not in the mood for asking any more questions."

The man is terrified as he realises you are not bluffing. He points at a door. "Through there."

» **If you wish to trust him, go to 4.**
» **If you have a reason to doubt him, go to 15.**

22

"We'll search individually," you tell the team. "I'll take this floor, the rest of you take the lower floor. Todd, we need access keys for the rooms."

Blackwood reaches into his equipment case and takes out a set of electronic key cards. "These will get you into any room." He passes them out to the team and you split up to search for whoever was listening in.

You head to a suite across the wide hallway. Gun ready, you slide the electronic key card into the lock of the first door. Inside, you move through the rooms, but there is no sign of anyone.

You head to the suite next to Mr Chen's. Again, you use the key card to open the door. You breathe deeply and get ready to enter...

» **Go to 37.**

23

You point at the map. "They are the initials of the stations," you say. "TY stands for Tsing Yi and SB stands for Sunny Bay, TC is Tung Chung and CC must stand for Cable Car."

The others nod in agreement. "A cable car goes to the Po Lin monastery," says Sun Lin. "There's a giant statue of Buddha there — it's a popular tourist attraction."

"It sounds like a good place for meeting someone... I'm certain that's where he was headed."

Perez looks down at the body. "He's not going there now."

"No, but we are... Bugs and Perez, I need you to do some legwork on Fang Da. See if you can find anything out about his involvement with the triads. Sun Lin and Todd, you're with me — we're heading for the cable car."

» **Go to 6.**

24

You hurry towards the cable car station and arrive at the pay desk before Sun Lin and the man. You pay for a ticket and get into a cabin. There are several other people in the cabin with you. The trip begins and you look down to see Sun Lin and the man getting into the following cabin on their own. You still have radio contact with Sun Lin and can hear her talking to the man.

Suddenly there is a scream. You look down and see the man attacking Sun Lin – he obviously didn't believe her. Sun Lin is fighting back, but you know it is only a matter of time before she is overcome. You have to make a quick decision.

» **To try to shoot at the man, go to 7.**
» **To try to get nearer, go to 18.**

25

"I need a holiday, boss. I was on the last case 24/7 for three weeks. I need a break. Can it wait?"

Tucker explodes with rage. "What do you mean by that? Let me tell you…" Tucker's shouting echoes round the cabin.

You hold the phone away from your ear. Perez winks and grins at you. When Tucker has finished ranting you place the phone back to your ear. "I'll take that as a 'no'."

"Take it as a warning," roars Tucker. "You signed up for Crime Team. If you don't want to take the case, then I'll get someone else to run the team."

"OK, sorry, boss. I'm exhausted, I made the wrong call."

"Too darn right you did!"

» **YOU'VE MADE A BAD DECISION!**
Make a note of this and go to 33.

26

"I'll go and get the team," you tell Sun Lin.

"That's a bad decision, boss," she replies. "We need to check out the evidence before it's destroyed." She points at the wastepaper bin.

You suddenly realise what she means! What was the man burning?

» **YOU MADE A BAD DECISION, *BUT YOU GOT AWAY WITH IT!***
Go to 17.

27

"OK, Todd, we'll do it your way," you say. "We don't pay yet. Mr Chen, if the kidnappers contact you again, stall – play for time. Meanwhile, we will look into this Fang Da character. We all need to look into the triad gangs."

At that moment Chen looks downwards.
Hmm, you think, there is a link between you and
the gangs. Looks like the Tiger is holding back on
us. You continue. "Sun Lin, you need to see what
you can come up with about the—"

Before you can finish, Bugs steps in front of
you and holds up a finger to his lips. He holds out
his smart phone and then points at the flashing red
light on the screen.

» **If you want to tell Bugs to put away his
phone, go to 11.**
» **If you want to wait to see what Bugs is
going to do, go to 41.**

28

"I think we should go to the police first," you tell
Tucker. "Like you said, Chen is a gangster and may
also be a traitor."

Tucker is not pleased with you. "I don't care
if he's a gangster or a boy scout! The man may
have valuable information! You go and talk to him
or I'll find someone who will! He's got a suite
at the Ritz Carlton Hotel. I'll arrange a meeting
for you in three hours – by then Sun Lin and
Blackwood will be there. You can all go and talk
to Chen. And remember we need to focus on
the kidnapping. The CIA is looking at his other

activities and we don't want to make him aware of that. Understand?"

The phone goes dead.

"We're going to see Mr Chen," you tell the team.

Bugs smiles. "You should have listened to me, boss, not Perez. He's the legs, I'm the brains."

Perez scowls, but you know Tucker is right. You have to talk to Chen.

» YOU MADE A BAD DECISION!

Make a note of this and go to 3.

29

"Fire and dragons go together," you say.

"And rubies are red, like fire…" adds Todd.

You nod. "Let's go – quietly." Everyone draws their weapons. You try the door – it's unlocked.

You all rush in. A man with a fiery dragon tattoo is sitting alone watching TV. He jumps up, but you have surprised him. "Hello, Mr Fang." You hit him with your gun and he drops to the floor. "OK, let's find Ruby and get out of here!" you say. Quickly, you search the apartment. You hear muffled cries coming from the next room. You rush in and find a girl tied up – it's Ruby!

Sun Lin unties her. "Don't worry, Ruby," she says, "we're going to take you back to your father."

"Even if he's as bad a man as the person who

kidnapped you…" whispers Perez.

You nod grimly: Perez is probably right, but your job was to rescue the girl, not sort out Mr "Tiger" Chen and his criminal activities.

"Good job," you tell the team. "Let's go." You sneak back down the stairs and all pile into a taxi. "I'll let Tucker know we've got Ruby." You take out your phone and contact your boss.

"Well done," says Tucker, "now I can move on it."

You wonder what he means as the taxi speeds you away safely down the street.

» **Go to 45.**

30

You signal to Sun Lin to follow you into the room. As you enter, you can smell burning. With your gun held at the ready, you move quickly into the main part of the suite, where there is a man burning paper in a wastepaper bin.

He sees you, leaps across the room and picks up a gun.

Before he can fire, Sun Lin shoots and hits him in the arm. The man drops his gun. You run over and kick it out of his reach.

He lies on the floor staring at you in hatred. On the table is a recording device – pair of headphones has fallen on the floor; the man is obviously the person who was listening to the microphone bug in Mr Chen's suite.

"Ask him who he's working for, and does he know anything about the kidnap," you tell Sun Lin.

Before she can ask, the man reaches into his pocket and slips a capsule into his mouth. As he bites on it, you try to remove it, but it is too late. The man groans and flops down dead.

"A suicide capsule," you mutter.

» If you wish to call the team together straight away, go to 26.
» If you wish to examine the dead man and the room for clues, go to 17.

31

"We pay up and get her back," you say. "The kidnapper might not be Fang Da and we've got nothing to go on. Paying the ransom will buy us time."

"No!" Chen stands up. "If this man is correct, my daughter will die anyway. I will have made Fang Da three million dollars richer for nothing. He will laugh at me and I will lose face among my associates. They will think I am a fool, that I have gone soft." He turns to you. "What sort of detective are you? It is up to you to find my daughter before she is harmed. I will not pay! If you make such a suggestion again, I will ask your boss to remove you from the case."

» YOU MADE A BAD DECISION!
Make a note of this and go to 27.

32

"Tell him Chen sent you," you say.

Sun Lin heads over to the man. You move closer to keep an eye on what is happening.

You hear her mention the name Chen. The man stares at her, before shaking his head. He turns and begins to move away. You realise that telling Sun Lin to mention Chen was a mistake.

"Say you have a message from Fang Da!" you

shout into the radio. But before Sun Lin can respond, the man has dashed into the crowd.

"Follow him!" you shout. You give chase, but it is hopeless, there are too many people around and you lose him.

"He said that he'd never heard of Chen," says Sun Lin.

You shake your head. "He was obviously lying – that's why he ran." You call Perez and Bugs, but they too have drawn a blank. You head back to the hotel.

» YOU MADE A BAD DECISION!
Make a note of this and go to 9.

33

"I'll take the case," you tell Tucker

"Too right you will," replies your boss. "You're going to Hong Kong.

"But the plane isn't heading to Hong Kong," you point out.

"It is now. The owner of the airline has just ordered it to be diverted. His name is Mr Samuel Chen. He is a very rich and powerful Hong Kong businessman. His daughter Ruby has been kidnapped. He needs our help."

"Why can't the Hong Kong police sort it out?" you ask.

"It's more than a simple kidnapping case. Chen is rumoured to be selling nuclear secrets to China, and to have links to the triads."

You give a low whistle. The triads are Chinese underworld gangs, and they're well known for their ruthlessness and illegal dealings.

Tucker continues. "We can't go public on this. We've had orders from the very top that Chen has to be helped. There's been no ransom demand yet, but we need to find out who has kidnapped the daughter and why. Then you've got to get her back in one piece. I'll fly out a couple of other members of the Crime Team to Hong Kong. Who do you want?"

You think. "Sun Lin is a must. She'll help out with translation and investigating the local community."

Tucker grunts. "So it's between Todd Blackwood and Anusha Das. Who do you want to choose?"

You have to decide between Das or Blackwood. You think about who would be best to help you investigate this case.

» **If you choose to take Todd Blackwood, go to 8.**
» **If you decide to take Anusha Das, go to 14.**

34

"We'll see what he has to say," you tell Sun Lin and Todd. "Let's go."

As you all move towards the man, he looks up. A look of concern flashes across his face – you suddenly realise that you have made a mistake – he knows who you are – he saw you at the airport! He turns and runs off through the crowd.

You give chase, but with so many people around it is hard to keep up with him. Eventually, you lose sight of him and he is gone.

You call Perez and Bugs, but they too have drawn a blank. You head back to the hotel to tell Chen that you have no leads.

» YOU MADE A BAD DECISION!
Make a note of it and go to 9.

35

"We need to interview Chen as soon as possible," you tell Tucker.

He grunts in agreement. "Chen lives in a suite at the Ritz Carlton Hotel. I'll arrange a meeting for you in three hours – by then Sun Lin and Blackwood will have arrived. You can all go and talk to him. And remember we need to focus on the kidnapping. The Central Intelligence Agency is looking at his other activities and we don't want to make him aware of that. Understand?"

"Sure thing, boss," you say.

"Keep me up to speed and don't forget who's really in charge!" says Tucker. He rings off.

You turn to Perez. "Bugs is right. We need to see Chen and find out what he knows about the kidnap. We'll wait for the others to arrive and then head to his hotel."

» Go to 3.

36

"Get over to Mong Kok and visit as many tailor's shops as you can," you tell Perez.

"But, boss, that's going to take forever!" Perez protests.

"Just do it, Leon," you snap and ring off. You tell Sun Lin what Perez told you.

"But, boss, we have a clue right here," she says. Sun Lin points at the ripped jacket. "Dragon Tailors, Mong Kok. We just need to find out its location…"

You look at the jacket and realise that you've made a big mistake. "I need to phone Perez," you sigh. You ring him.

"Leon, I'm sorry I made a mistake…"

» YOU MADE A BAD DECISION!

Make a note of it and go to 21.

37

You enter the room. As you make your way further in, you see a recording device and a set of headphones on a table. You realise that this must be the room being used to listen to Chen in the suite next door.

Suddenly, you hear a noise behind you. As you spin around you hold out your gun, but you are not fast enough. The man takes you by surprise! He smashes you on the head with something heavy, and you crash to the floor in a heap. Your world is spinning as blood pours from your cut forehead. Dazed, you look up into the barrel of a pistol. Then there is a white-hot flash and a crack. You feel a searing pain, then it quickly fades to nothing.

» **You found the man who was listening to Chen, but it has cost you your life. You have failed! Start this case again by going back to 1.**

38

The plane lands at Hong Kong's busy airport and you make your way through customs. You flash your Crime Team identification badge at the officers on duty and they wave you through.

You walk through into the airport arrivals

lounge where there are several people holding up name cards as they wait to greet people. Two of these people catch your eye.

Which of these do you wish to approach?

» If you wish to talk to the woman with long hair, go to 19.

» If you wish to talk to the man with spiky hair, go to 43.

39

You point at the man standing near the ticket office. "That man there with spiky hair. I'm sure he was at the airport, when I arrived. He was holding up a dragon sign."

Todd shakes his head. "That's not a lot to go on."

"It's the only lead we've got…"

"Maybe Leon and Bugs have found something," replies Todd.

» To contact Bugs and Perez, go to 13.

» To send Sun Lin to approach the man, go to 2.

» If you decide that you should all approach the man, go to 34.

40

You ring Tucker and tell him what has happened.

"Looks like we've drawn a blank," you say.

Tucker explodes with fury! "You've got a dead man that can be linked to Fang Da and you've got some burnt paper — use some of that high-tech equipment that you asked me to buy! Don't ring me again until you've got something to report — or you're off the case and you'll be swimming home, because I won't be paying your airfare!"

The phone goes dead.

» **YOU'VE RECEIVED A WARNING FROM TUCKER!**

Make a note of this and go to 10.

41

Bugs holds out his smart phone and moves towards a picture on the wall. He stands in front of it.

You hear Perez mutter under his breath, "No time to be admiring artwork."

Then Bugs reaches under the frame and pulls at something. He turns around and holds up a small microphone, before smashing it to pieces on a very expensive-looking table. "It's a bug. Someone has been listening in," he says.

Chen is puzzled. "How could you tell that was there on your phone?" he asks.

Bugs smiles. "The phone is a little more than that. This was a short-range device, anyone who

was listening in must be nearby. They will be in one of the rooms on this floor or below."

Chen snaps. "I will send my guards."

You shake your head. "We'll do this. I need our weapons back, please…"

Mr Chen agrees and soon you have your guns back in your possession.

» **If you wish to search the rooms individually, go to 22.**

» **If you want to split the team into two groups, go to 16.**

42

"I think it's the earth symbol," you say. You head to the door.

Todd quickly pulls you back. "No, boss, it's got to be the fire symbol. Think about it. What does Fang Da call himself?"

You think about this for a second and realise that Todd is right. How could you be so stupid? You nearly made a fatal error.

» **YOU MADE A BAD DECISION!**
   Make a note of it and go to 29.

43

You point at the man. "I think that's our contact," you say. You, Perez and Bugs head over to the man.

"Crime Team?" he asks. You nod.

"Follow me, please." The man leads the three of you out of the airport and into the car park. He heads to a white passenger van. "This is our transport," he tells you.

"No limo?" asks Perez.

Before you can say anything, the doors of the van burst open and three men with guns leap out. There is no time to react as they open fire.

You feel a searing pain in your shoulder and fall to the floor, unconscious.

» Go to 5.

44

"They are the initials of the stations," you say. "Look – TY stands for Tsing Yi and SB stands for Sunny Bay. Then he was supposed to be going onto Disneyland for a meeting at 3 p.m. today. Look at the map!"

"Hang on, boss," says Perez. "What about the other initials? TC and CC – surely they stand for Tung Chung and Cable Car?"

You look at the map. Perez is right.

Sun Lin nods. "There's a cable car that goes to the Po Lin monastery. There's a statue of a giant Buddha there. It's a top tourist attraction. It would be a good place for meeting someone…"

You realise that you made a mistake in front of the team. You swallow your pride. "OK, you're right. Bugs and Perez, I need you to do some legwork on Fang Da. See if you can find anything out about his involvement with the triads. Tell Chen we've got a lead and to keep in touch. Sun Lin and Todd, you're with me – we're heading for the cable car."

» **YOU MADE A BAD DECISION!**
   Make a note of it and go to 6.

45

You are soon back at Chen's suite, where Ruby is reunited with her father.

"Thank you and your team," he says. "I am glad that you brought Ruby back safely or there would have been grave consequences. Goodbye." He dismisses you with a wave of his hand.

And thank you too – so much – you think as you head out of the apartment onto the landing.

Perez shakes his head. "Of all the ungrateful…"

You stand waiting in the lobby as a lift arrives. A group of policemen burst out of the lift doors as soon as they open. They break down the door of Chen's apartment. From inside you hear shouting and the sounds of fighting.

"Let's get out of here," you tell the team. "I think the Tiger is about to be caged!"

Some minutes later you are in the hotel reception watching a group of policemen taking Chen and his henchmen away. He looks furious.

"Poor Ruby," says Sun Lin. "She gets taken away and on her return, her father gets arrested!"

"She's got her mother," you reply grimly. "And to be honest, he wasn't much of a father…"

The phone rings. It is Tucker. "Did you see Mr Chen's homecoming party?"

"Yes. What was that all about?"

Tucker laughs. "Someone told the Chinese authorities that Mr 'Tiger' Chen has been selling their secrets. I think he's going away on a trip…"

"Talking of trips," you say. "I want a holiday."

"You can have one, once you get back here and sort out the paperwork," grunts Tucker. "I've booked you all on a flight back to the US."

"First class?" you ask hopefully.

"Not a chance," replies Tucker. "Not a chance…"

» You've cracked the case – well done!
Go to 46 to see how you rate as a detective…

46

How do you rate as a
Crime Team detective?

WASHOUT – if you FAILED or were THROWN OFF
THE CASE.
Polish up your detective skills and go back to 1.

AMATEUR – at least ONE WARNING.
You need to try harder. See if you can do better on
other CRIME TEAM cases.

 ONE-STAR AGENT – no warnings, but made THREE
or more BAD DECISIONS.
You need to boost your detecting skills. See if you can
stay more alert on other CRIME TEAM cases.

✪ ✪ **TWO-STAR AGENT –** no warnings, but made TWO
BAD DECISIONS.
Maybe you're lacking in confidence. Try looking for less
help on other CRIME TEAM cases.

✪ ✪ ✪ **THREE-STAR AGENT –** no warnings, but made
ONE BAD DECISION.
You're a worthy leader of CRIME TEAM – well done!
But can you do as well on other CRIME TEAM cases?

★ **FIRST-CLASS CRIME TEAM AGENT –** no warnings,
and made no bad decisions.
You're a genius detective! Bet you can't do as well on
other CRIME TEAM cases…

Want to read more "You Are The Hero" adventures? Well, why not try these...

Also by the 2Steves: iHorror
Fight your fear. Choose your fate.

978 1 40830 985 8 pb
978 1 40831 476 0 eBook

978 1 40830 986 5 pb
978 1 40831 477 7 eBook

978 1 40830 988 9 pb
978 1 40831 479 1 eBook

978 1 40830 987 2 pb
978 1 40831 478 4 eBook

BATTLE BOOKS

by Gary Smailes

Take up your weapons and prepare to fight your own battle...

978 1 4451 0112 5

978 1 4451 0113 2

978 1 4451 0114 9

978 1 4451 0115 6

978 0 7496 9286 5   978 0 7496 9285 8

In *City of Terror* you must solve the clues to stop a terrorist attack in London. But who is planning the attack, and when will it take place? It's a race against time!

In *Russian Gold* an armoured convoy has been attacked in Moscow and hundreds of gold bars stolen. But who was behind the raid, and where is the gold? Get to Russia, get the clues and get the gold.